THE COMPLETE ORGAN PLAYER
SOLID GOLD CLASSICS BOOK TWO

Wise Publications
London/New York/Sydney

Exclusive Distributors:
Music Sales Limited
8/9 Frith Street,
London W1V 5TZ, England.
Music Sales Pty Limited
120 Rothschild Avenue,
Rosebery, NSW 2018,
Australia.

This book © Copyright 1992 by Wise Publications
Order No.AM84609
ISBN 0-7119-2632-8

Cover design and illustration by Pearce Marchbank Studio
Compiled by Peter Evans
Arranged by Kenneth Baker
Music processed by MSS Studios

Music Sales' complete catalogue lists thousands of
titles and is free from your local music shop, or direct from
Music Sales Limited.
Please send a cheque/postal order for £1.50 for postage to:
Music Sales Limited, Newmarket Road, Bury St. Edmunds,
Suffolk IP33 3YB.

Your Guarantee of Quality
As publishers, we strive to produce every book to the highest
commercial standards.
The music has been freshly engraved and the book has been
carefully designed to minimise awkward page turns and to make
playing from it a real pleasure.
Particular care has been given to specifying acid-free, neutral-
sized paper which has not been chlorine bleached but produced with
special regard for the environment. Throughout, the printing and
binding have been planned to ensure a sturdy, attractive
publication which should give years of enjoyment.
If your copy fails to meet our high standards, please inform us and
we will gladly replace it.

Printed in the United Kingdom by
J.B. Offset Printers (Marks Tey) Limited, Marks Tey, Essex.

A Woman In Love 20
Catch A Falling Star 10
Claudette 36
From A Distance 30
I'll Know 4
If Not For You 12
MacArthur Park 38
Message To Michael 8
More Than I Can Say 32
My Kind Of Girl 41
Oh, Lonesome Me 18
Portrait Of My Love 6
The First Time Ever I Saw Your Face 24
The Look Of Love 26
(They Long To Be) Close To You 22
Too Young 14
Walk On By 34
When I Fall In Love 28
Wonderful Tonight 16

Chord Charts 44, 45, 46, 47

I'LL KNOW
Words & Music by Frank Loesser

Upper: clarinet
Lower: flutes
Pedal: 8'
Drums: bossa nova ♩ = 92

PORTRAIT OF MY LOVE

Words by David West. Music by Cyril Ornadel

Upper: horn
Lower: flutes
Pedal: 8'
Drums: swing ♩ = 100

MESSAGE TO MICHAEL

Words by Hal David. Music by Burt Bacharach

Upper: violin
Lower: flutes
Pedal: bass guitar
Drums: 8 beat

CATCH A FALLING STAR
Words & Music by Paul Vance & Lee Pockriss

Upper: flute + percussion
Lower: flutes + piano
Pedal: 8'
Drums: cha-cha ♩ = 112

11

IF NOT FOR YOU

Words & Music by Bob Dylan

Upper: oboe
Lower: flutes
Pedal: 8'
Drums: rock   ♩ = 104

TOO YOUNG
Words by Sylvia Dee. Music by Sid Lippman

Upper: saxophone
Lower: flutes + piano
Pedal: 8′
Drums: swing

WONDERFUL TONIGHT
Words & Music by Eric Clapton

Upper: guitar
Lower: flutes
Pedal: bass guitar
Drums: rock   ♩ = 100

OH, LONESOME ME
Words & Music by Don Gibson

Upper: violin
Lower: flutes + piano
Pedal: 8'
Drums: swing   ♩ = 208

A WOMAN IN LOVE

Words & Music by Barry Gibb & Robin Gibb

Upper: string ensemble
Lower: flute
Pedal: bass guitar
Drums: rock   ♩ = 96

(THEY LONG TO BE) CLOSE TO YOU

Words by Hal David. Music by Burt Bacharach

Upper: piano (with sustain)
Lower: flutes
Pedal: bass guitar
Drums: 8 beat ♩ = 84

Lyrics:

Why do birds sud-den-ly ap-pear ev-'ry time you are near?
Why do stars fall down from the sky ev-'ry time you walk by?
Why all the boys in town fol-low you all a-round.

Just like me, they long to be close to you.
Just like me, they long to be close to you.
Just like me, they long to be close to you.

Why do

On the day that you were born, the an-gels got to-geth-er and de-

cid - ed to cre - ate a dream come true. So they sprink-led moon-dust in your hair of

cresc.

gold, and star - light in your eyes of blue. That is

D.S. al Coda
Upper: add strings

⊕ **CODA**

close to you. _____ Ah _____

Close to you. _____

(Repeat and fade)

23

THE FIRST TIME EVER I SAW YOUR FACE

Words & Music by Ewan MacColl

Upper: string ensemble
Lower: flutes
Pedal: 8'
Drums: 8 beat ♩ = 84

THE LOOK OF LOVE

Words by Hal David. Music by Burt Bacharach

Upper: synth.
Lower: flutes + piano
Pedal: bass guitar
Drums: 8 beat   ♩ = 112

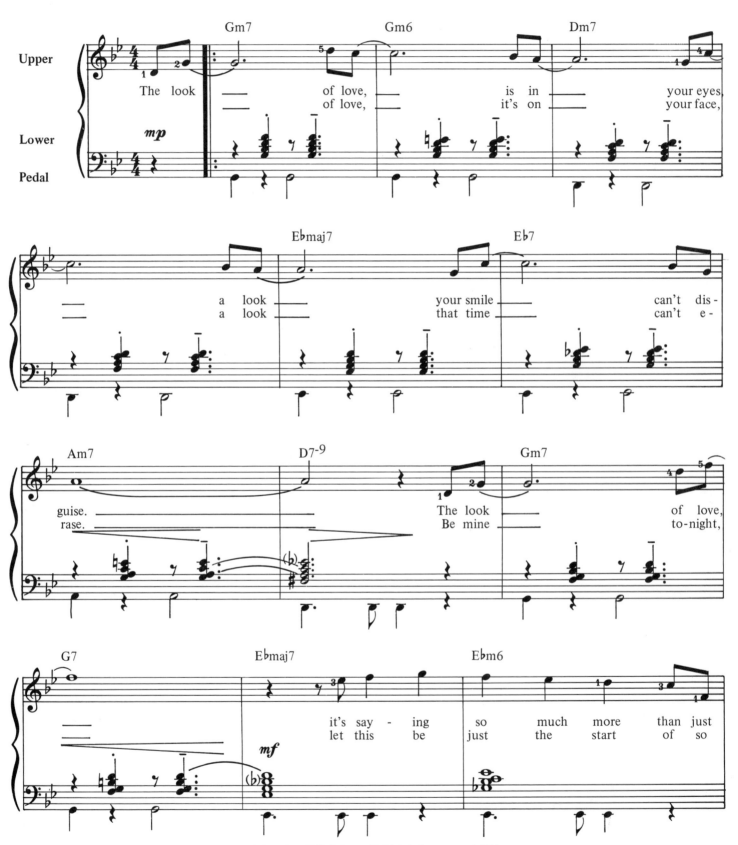

WHEN I FALL IN LOVE
Music by Victor Young. Words by Edward Heyman

Upper: oboe
Lower: flutes
Pedal: 16' + 8'
Drums: swing ♩ = 92

* Gm7 on E♭ pedal

FROM A DISTANCE
Words & Music by Julie Gold

Upper: guitar
Lower: flutes
Pedal: bass guitar
Drums: 8 beat   ♩ = 88

MORE THAN I CAN SAY

Words & Music by Sonny Curtis & Jerry Allison

Upper: guitar
Lower: flutes + piano
Pedal: bass guitar
Drums: rock $\quad \downarrow = 112$

WALK ON BY

Music by Burt Bacharach. Words by Hal David

Upper: trumpet + string ensemble
Lower: flutes
Pedal: bass guitar
Drums: 8 beat   ♩ = 104

CLAUDETTE
Words & Music by Roy Orbison

Upper: jazz organ (with tremolo)
Lower: flutes + piano
Pedal: bass guitar
Drums: rock   ♩ = 120

MACARTHUR PARK
Words & Music by Jimmy Webb

Upper: flute
Lower: flutes
Pedal: bass guitar
Drums: 8 beat ♩ = 92

MY KIND OF GIRL

Words & Music by Leslie Bricusse

Upper: piano
Lower: flutes
Pedal: 8'
Drums: swing ♩ = 120

CHORD CHARTS (For Left Hand)

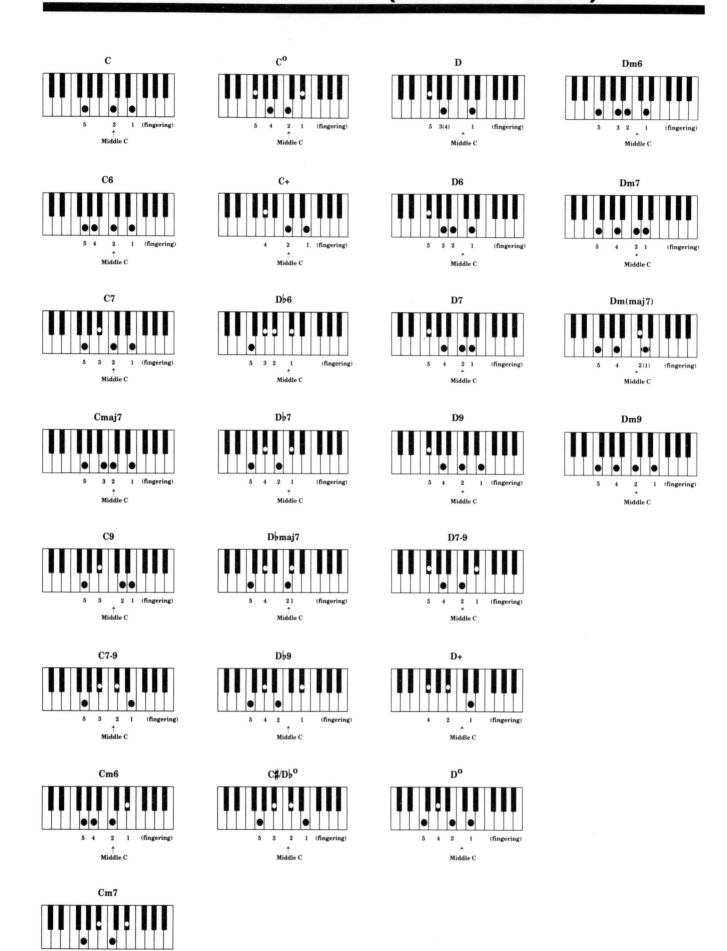

CHORD CHARTS (For Left Hand)

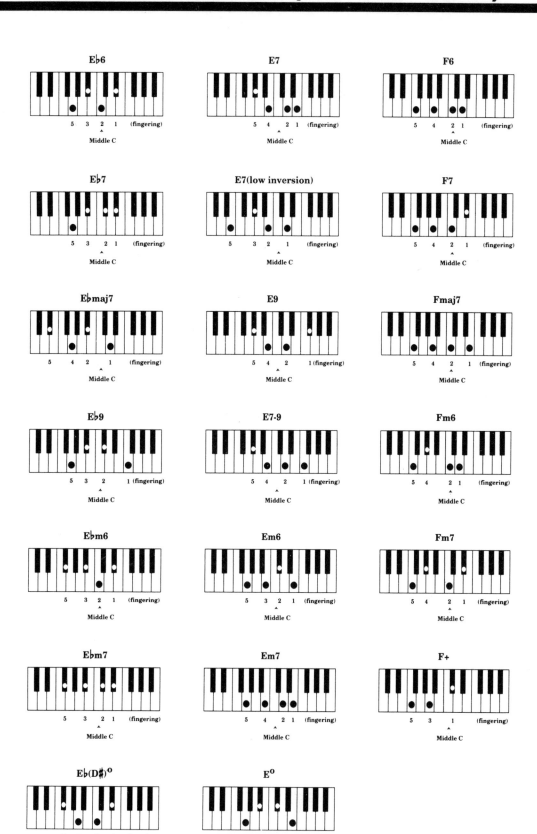

CHORD CHARTS (For Left Hand)

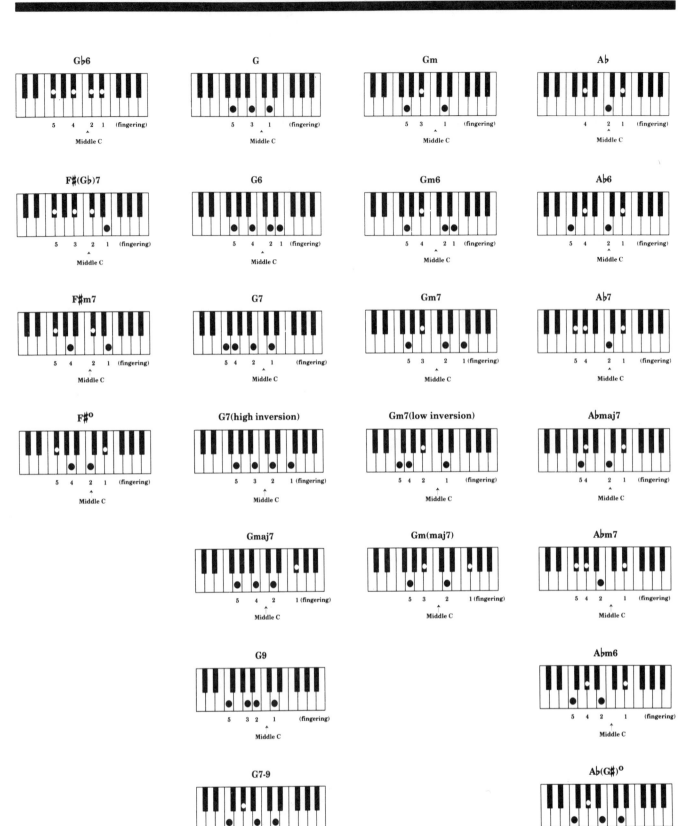

CHORD CHARTS (For Left Hand)

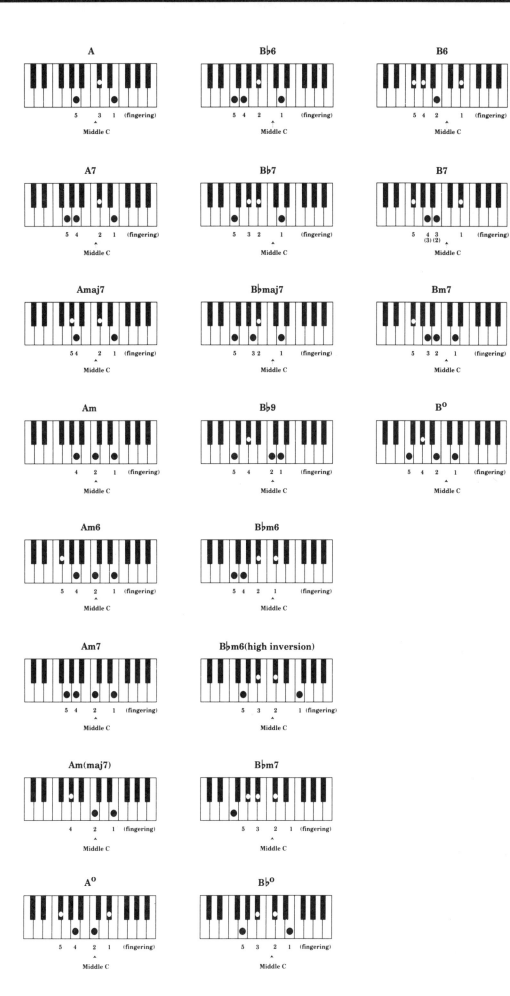